D1362245

THE RABINOWITZ COLLECTION

COVER: *Allegory of Intemperance* by Hieronymus Bosch, Netherlandish,

c. 1450–1516. Oil on wood-panel, 13 5/16 x 12⅛ inches.

INTRODUCTION AND COMMENTARY

BY CHARLES SEYMOUR, JR.

Curator of Renaissance Art,

Professor of the History of Art

YALE UNIVERSITY ART GALLERY

THE RABINOWITZ COLLECTION OF EUROPEAN PAINTINGS

REF
N
590
.A7
Cop. 1

The most important single gift received by the Yale Art Gallery in 1959 was the collection of twenty-eight paintings presented by Hannah D. and the late Louis M. Rabinowitz, industrialist and philanthropist.

The paintings, together with five others previously given, making a total of thirty-three, include from the Northern Renaissance a fine composition by the Netherlandish painter, Hieronymus Bosch, a panel by the great German artist, Lucas Cranach, the Elder, a miniature portrait by another famous German, Hans Holbein, the Younger, and a vigorous sketch by Anthony Van Dyck. All four of these works are the first by these respective artists to enter the Art Gallery collection. Among the Italian paintings in the bequest are: panels of Prophets *from the celebrated Carmelite altarpiece by Pietro Lorenzetti of 1329; a* Madonna Annunciate *from an altarpiece by the fifteenth-century Sienese painter, Sassetta; a* Madonna *by the Venetian, Bartolommeo Vivarini, and a large ceiling decoration by the Venetian eighteenth-century artist, Giovanni Battista Tiepolo, assisted by his son.*

In 1871 the Yale Art Gallery was greatly enriched by the acquisition of the now famous Jarves Collection of medieval and Renaissance paintings. By his gifts in the 1920's and 30's and his bequest of 1943 Maitland F. Griggs, B.A. 1896, strengthened the Jarves Collection through numerous Italian paintings and sculptures of the same period. Now, with the addition of the Rabinowitz Collection, a number of quite important gaps in these first two collections have been filled, particularly in the areas of Flemish and German painting.

In 1952, when the Yale Alumni Board established the annual Yale Medal awards for outstanding service to the University, Louis Rabinowitz was in the first group so honored. His citation read: "Mr. Rabinowitz came to this country from Lithuania at the age of 14. He has been the emigrant's dream fulfilled through imagination, industry, and integrity. He has believed in Yale and has shown it by strengthening our libraries and Gallery, and by fostering research in many fields. During its 250 years Yale has had no benefactor more discerning of its mission as a University."

ANDREW CARNDUFF RITCHIE

DIRECTOR

INTRODUCTION

The earliest of the paintings given to the Yale Art Gallery by Hannah D. and the late Louis M. Rabinowitz come from the Italian *Trecento*. No one today would seriously consider calling them, as was once the fashion, "Italian Primitives". As a class such pictures are by no means primitive in the sense of crude beginnings; instead they represent the peak of a long development. Far from rough gropings, they are the highly sophisticated and deftly stylized product of a system combining eloquent line and delicate colors brought to a maximum of saturation and brilliance. Painted in the styles of individualized masters, aided in turn by highly trained journeymen and carefully selected apprentices, they seem so sure and controlled that there is often danger of overlooking the extraordinary union of craftsman's skill and poet's sensitivity required for their creation.

With the cleaning and rehabilitation of the Rabinowitz Italian paintings, which has been well begun by Mr. Andrew Petryn, assisted by Mr. Charles Tauss, of the Gallery staff, qualities of character and variety in this mode of 14th-century painting are emerging ever more clearly to our view. To take one example, it is possible within the Rabinowitz collection alone to make a kind of cross-section of the period centering in *10–11* 1330, by comparing the *Madonna,* now attributed to Niccolò di Segna, and the *Apos-* *12–13* *tles and Prophet* largely by Pietro Lorenzetti (Sienese artists) with the panels of *Sts. John the Baptist and Mary Magdalen,* from *14–15* the Venetian School, attributed to Paolo Veneziano. To this trio we might add the only slightly later *Coronation of the Virgin* of the School of Rimini (a mid-point between Venice, Padua and Florence). Of artists of the succeeding generation it is possible in the Rabinowitz Collection to compare the "expressionist" Simone de' Crocifissi of Bologna with the "classicist" Jacopo di Cione of Florence. And finally in *16–17* two altar wings by Giovanni dal Ponte of Florence there is to be seen a handsome example of the juncture of the *Trecento* Italian tradition with late Gothic influences from Northern Europe toward 1410.

Thus one may sense the flow and intermingling of currents of regional styles that make Italian medieval and Renaissance art so endlessly fascinating and so much themselves. There is really no way of separating the Middle Ages from the Renaissance in Italian art. An imaginary line of division between the two periods makes no sense here, for the medieval practices of technique and habits of vision continued, according to region, deep into the 15th century. This is to a point true of Florence, illustrated by *18–19* the graceful forms of the little jewel-like *Annunciation* and the marriage salver dec- *20–21* orated with imagery drawn from courtly love—both of about 1425/30. And in Siena, at precisely the same date, time seems suspended for a breathless moment in the startlingly beautiful *Virgin Annunciate* by *22–23* the artist we have come to know affectionately as Sassetta. A medieval mystical and pietistic strain, finally, pervaded the now dismembered composition of which the fragmentary head and shoulders of the Christ (once ascribed to Castagno, but far more probably by the so-called Master of San Miniato) was once a part.

But there is a new outlook in a series of paintings coming from Venice and the Veneto shortly after 1470. There is a hint of this in two intriguing panels, once in the Woodward Collection in London, from a now dispersed altarpiece dedicated to St. Mammas and believed by some to have been painted by the mysterious Veronese-Venetian, Francesco dei Franceschi. It is felt unmistakably in the small *Madonna* given by many authorities to Giovanni Bellini and in the even more impressive *Madonna*

24–25 of Bellini's contemporary, Bartolommeo Vivarini. A little panel of *St. Peter* by Carlo

26–27 Crivelli (who was active in Venice and the Marches) fairly crackles with humanist energy, and the small *Madonna* attributed to Pintoricchio shows as a detail a charming interpretation of an antique Roman relief.

This brings us in date to the *Gambaro*

28–29 *Madonna* (signed and dated 1495) by Francia, the "Bolognese Eclectic" *avant la lettre;* one can see plainly here the importance of Francia for the supreme Raphael's early style, even to the Northern type of landscape with distant cities sprouting sharply-pointed Gothic spires. Beyond Raphael and the High Renaissance there looms Giuliano Bugiardini's masterpiece in portraiture painted toward 1540 in what

30–31 is called the Mannerist style: the monumental seated figure of the great Florentine Renaissance historian, Francesco Guicciardini.

Two other 16th-century Renaissance portraits deserve special mention. The first portrays a handsome, bearded young man be-

32–33 side a geographer's globe in the dark costume known as "Spanish black", characteristic of the period between 1540–50. The picture has recently been cleaned, bringing out, in spite of considerable signs of rubbing, damage and wear, the superlative quality of the conception and mastery of execution. The painting is signed by Titian and it would appear to be identical.with a portrait, once in the Collection of Charles I of England, catalogued as "by Tician". A 17th-century catalogue-notice of the King's paintings describes with great care a "mans Picture" with a "gloab Standing by him upon a table with his right elbowe lyeing upon part of a table...." As in our picture, the subject is described as wearing a "black habbitt", and the subject (like ours again, "half a figure Soe bigg as yᵉ life") is specified as painted on canvas ("opan cloth"). After the dispersal of the king's famous collection under the Commonwealth the portrait of this "Man with a Gloab" by "Tician" vanishes. Only recently has it begun to seem possible to pick up the picture's history again. As we see it now, the painting has been cut down somewhat, but its originally squarish proportions must have been very close to the 3' 3" x 3' 2" in Belgic feet in the 17th-century inventory.

Comparable in scale and quality is a seated figure of a scholar attributed to Tin-

34–35 toretto. This portrait is unfinished and as such is valuable as an index to the painting methods of the later 16th century.

Let us turn now to another aspect of the Rabinowitz Collection—the representation of trends in North European as distinct from Italian painting. Two small panels of the *Fall* and *Sacrifice of Isaac* belong in this category. Even though at one time they were attributed to the Florentine Mariotto Albertinelli, they seem to be quite clearly Flemish paintings based on Florentine Renaissance compositions from about 1510–20. Completely Northern in all respects, however, is the beautiful fragment of a larger composition which all authorities today agree in giving to the Netherlandish master Hieronymus Bosch.

36–39   This painting presents Bosch's usual trenchant satire on human foibles, and here it is obviously the sin of gluttony that is being castigated. The ensemble of which this fragment originally may have been a part is still in question. It is of interest, however, that the dimension of width is within an eighth of an inch of the Bosch panel depicting a banquet in a small boat in the Louvre, known as the "Ship of Fools", which has much the same subject matter. Did the Rabinowitz panel belong to the Louvre panel in some way? Were both parts of the same image which at some time was cut into two parts? Research in this direction is proceeding and it seems probable that a more definite conclusion may soon be the result. It is exciting, in any event, to consider the possibilities of further discovery in this phase of Bosch scholarship.

40–41   The Northern Renaissance group continues with a *Crucifixion,* with strong religio-political overtones, by Lucas Cranach, the Elder, and with a miniature of a young

42–43   man from the English Period of Hans Holbein, the Younger. Representing France, or possibly the Low Countries, toward 1570, there is a complex figure-group glowing in

44–45   russets, yellows, pinks and blacks, adapted from one of Primaticcio's most famous designs for the decoration of the royal Chateau of Fontainebleau.

   Our review of the collection concludes with the small-scale *"modello"* attributed

46–47   to the 17th-century Flemish artist, Anton Van Dyck, a work related to a great altarpiece by that painter in Antwerp, and with

48–53   three masterly compositions from the studio and brush of the Venetian 18th-century *virtuoso,* Tiepolo. One of these paintings was executed in Germany in collaboration with his son.

   In the commentary on the illustrated paintings which follows, no attempt has been made to prepare a definitive catalogue. It is hoped only that the references and data on physical properties may assist in future study. I would like to acknowledge here the advice of a colleague who is Curator of Prints in the Art Gallery, Professor Egbert Haverkamp-Begemann; he has kindly read the entries for the Northern paintings. Stanton Loomis Catlin, our Assistant Director, has been tireless in the task of editing all the text for publication. Two members of the Renaissance Seminar in the Yale Graduate Studies in Art History, Mrs. Charles Welles and Miss Nancy Gaylord, have ably assisted in the checking of references and in the writing of basic drafts for many of the commentaries. The catalogue of the Rabinowitz Collection by Professor Lionello Venturi, privately printed in 1945, has been consulted constantly. In all references this work is abbreviated in the following manner: "L. Venturi, 1945."

NICCOLO DI SEGNA (?)

(Sienese, active about 1330–1340)
Madonna and Child. Cleaned, 1955
Tempera on wood-panel, 45½ x 28¼

For some time attributed to Duccio, or his school, this *Madonna* (from about 1330) represents a strain of painting in Siena really quite different from Duccio's. The artist, possibly Niccolò di Segna, inherited the languid poses, the elongated but heavy forms, and the relaxed swing of line from his father, Segna di Bonaventura, a follower and rival of Duccio. Pointing to a period even earlier than Segna's are the saints in the background with their decorative and hieratic function, and the ornamented brocade and throne. Contrasting with these archaic elements is the human aspect of the mother nursing the Child, a motive which appears here possibly for the first time in Sienese *Trecento* painting. The panel was in the monastery of S. Eugenio, near Siena, until it was sold about the year 1912.

COLLECTION:
From S. Eugenio, Siena, to Dan Fellows Platt, Englewood, New Jersey.

EXHIBITIONS:
Phillips Memorial Gallery, Washington, D.C., 1941; New York, 1955 (E. and A. Silberman).

REFERENCES:
B. Berenson, *Central Italian Painters,* 1897, p. 140, and 1909, p. 163 (Duccio).
F. M. Perkins, *Art in America,* VIII, 1920, p. 199 (school of Duccio).
R. Van Marle, *Italian Schools,* II, 1924, p. 143 (follower of Segna).
L. Venturi, *Pitture Italiane in America,* 1931, pl. XXIII.
B. Berenson, *Italian Pictures,* 1932, p. 523 (Segna di Bonaventura).
G. Edgell, *Sienese Painting,* 1932, p. 64 (a contemporary of Ambrogio Lorenzetti).
L. Venturi, 1945, pp. 1–2 (follower of Duccio).

PIETRO LORENZETTI

(Sienese, active 1320–1348)

St. Andrew and St. James the Greater with a Prophet

Tempera on wood-panel, 14½ x 8½ (St. Andrew); 14⅝ x 8⅝ (St. James the Greater); 22 x 21½ (frame, with Prophet). Cleaned, 1959

These two half-length apostles with the head and shoulders of an Old Testament prophet in the framing have a distinguished origin. Along with two other pairs of apostles (Nos. 62 and 64 in the Academy at Siena) our panels very probably belonged to the upper part of the altarpiece painted by Pietro Lorenzetti in 1329, for the Carmelite church in Siena (S. Maria del Monte Carmelo). The central panel, with the predella panel below it, was removed to the Oratory of Sant' Ansano in Castelnuovo Berardenga, close to Siena, as early as the 16th century. The rest of the altarpiece remained with the Carmelites in Siena who disposed of parts of it in the 19th century. It may be assumed that there were originally six framed pairs of apostles similar to the grouping reproduced on the opposite page, but exactly when our picture left the Carmelites and through whose hands it passed afterwards is not recorded. An interesting aspect of the Rabinowitz picture is that apparently the *St. Andrew* and the *Prophet* were done by the master himself, while its companion was painted by the hand of an assistant. Such division of labor was frequent in Medieval and Renaissance art.

EXHIBITION:

New York, 1955 (E. and A. Silberman).

REFERENCES:

L. Venturi, 1945, pp. 3-4.

E. Carli, *Les Sienois,* Paris, 1957, p. 38.

13

PAOLO VENEZIANO

(Venetian, active about 1320–1360)

St. Mary Magdalen and *St. John the Baptist*
Tempera on wood-panels, 23 x 9⅜ (St. Mary
Magdalen); 23¼ x 9¼ (St. John the Baptist).
Cleaned, 1959

Inscribed: St. Mary Magdelen: MARIA M; St.
John the Baptist (scroll): ECCE AGNU[S] ECCE
QUI TOLLIS PEC[C]ATA

These panels, probably dating from the 1330's,
are examples of the earliest Venetian painting
which began to break away from the Byzantine
domination. Elements of that Eastern medieval
style are still very evident in the strength of
the color, the immobility of the pose and the
sobriety of expression, especially the haggard,
emaciated St. John. Latin, however, has re-
placed Greek on the inscription of his scroll,
indicating the triumph of a Western European consciousness in Venice. The line, which
is fine and spidery, has more grace and tension
than the Byzantine; and Gothic influences,
seen in the super-elongation of forms and the
swing of the drapery, show a livelier and
more human outlook than the Eastern tradition would have allowed. The faïence oint-
ment jar held by The Magdalen is decorated
with a Near-Eastern pattern.

COLLECTION:
Museo Guidi, Faenza (?).
REFERENCES:
L. Venturi, 1945, pp. 11–12.
B. Berenson, *Italian Pictures of the Renais-
sance, Venetian Paintings,* I, 1957, p. 128.

GIOVANNI DI MARCO, called DAL PONTE

(Florentine, 1385–1437)

St. John the Baptist and Crucifixion
St. James Major and Resurrection

Tempera on wood-panels, 50⅛ x 12⅞ (St. John the Baptist and Crucifixion); 50¼ x 13 (St. James Major and Resurrection).

Inscribed: St. John the Baptist (scroll): ECCE ANGNUS D[E]I

This pair of paintings decorated the wings of an altarpiece. The artist, Giovanni di Marco, was called Giovanni dal Ponte because he had an active workshop near the Ponte Vecchio in Florence. He was a part of the generation of Florentine painters working in the early 15th century whose main impetus came from the century before. Some of the delicacy and sweetness of the late 14th century in Florence appears in the light pink and grey of the saints' mantles and in the gentle sway of their poses. But the rhythm of the drapery, especially in the St. James, reflects a more positive energy resulting from the new vitality of the Gothic "International Style", coming to Italy from the North.

EXHIBITION:
New York, 1917 (F. Kleinberger).

REFERENCES:
O. Sirén and Brockwell, *Catalogue of a Loan Exhibition of Italian Primitives,* 1917, p. 42 (see above).

F. M. Perkins, *Art in America,* IX, 1921, p. 148.

R. Van Marle, *Italian Schools,* IX, 1927, p. 86.

L. Venturi, 1945, pp. 17–18.

FLORENTINE (15th century)

The Annunciation
Tempera on wood-panel, 7½ x 11

This Virgin and Angel Gabriel were originally painted on separate panels, probably at the summits of the wings of a small altarpiece. The Angel approaches rapidly with swirling draperies and outspread wings. His vigor contrasts strongly with the composure of the Virgin. The dignity of her pose and the classic beauty of her delicately chiselled profile give her a monumentality remarkable in so tiny a figure. The porcelain-like quality of the painted surface and the delicate plasticity of the forms point to the Florentine school toward 1430. The painting was formerly attributed to Fra Filippo Lippi, but the style reflects the charm of Masolino and the grace of Fra Angelico. It is essentially that of the "Master of the Griggs Crucifixion" (so named after the painting in the Metropolitan Museum of Art, New York, which may have belonged to the same ensemble as our *Annunciation* figures).

COLLECTIONS:
Albertini, Pistoia; Sir Charles Townley, 1877; Lady Crosslay, Somerset, England.
EXHIBITION:
Phillips Memorial Gallery, Washington, D.C., 1941.
REFERENCE:
L. Venturi, 1945, p. 15.

Marriage Salver
Tempera on wood-panel, 22⅞ diameter

This type of salver, which can be dated on stylistic grounds about 1420–25, was designed for ceremonial presentation of wedding gifts. The imagery is related to the late medieval theme of courtly love. The figures of noble ladies and gentlemen are dressed in rich garments of scarlet, dark green, rose, vermilion, and brown, strikingly set off against the monochrome gray-brown of the background. In the center of the picture a group of young ladies in the guise of the chaste goddess Diana and her nymphs point their arrows at a wounded hart. The hart symbolizes the groom, now changed, like Actaeon, from the free hunter he once was into the prize of a chaste love. Around the central scene we see other noble couples in amorous dalliance. Both the allegorical subject matter and the vivacious linear forms are characteristic of the courtly international Gothic style which captivated Florentine taste in the early 15th century.

REFERENCE:
L. Venturi, 1945, p. 19.

STEFANO DI GIOVANNI, called SASSETTA

(Sienese, mentioned 1423–1450)

The Virgin Annunciate
Tempera on wood-panel, 23¼ x 19⅝

This *Virgin Annunciate* expresses very nearly all the lyricism of the painter's religious and esthetic fervor. The graceful pose, the flowing linear folds of drapery and the gesture of the delicately modelled hands create a sense of motion in a magical space.

The dating of this well-known little panel, evidently once a pinnacle of a large altarpiece, has been disputed. Some have seen a Gothicizing tendency here, but the consensus of scholarship associates this figure and a companion *Angel* in the town of Massa Marittima, with the tridimensional forms and sophisticated system of interlocking curves of the *Madonna of the Snows,* painted between 1430 and 1432 for the Chapel of St. Boniface in the Cathedral of Siena. On the whole it seems likely that our panel was originally part of that altarpiece, which remained intact in the Cathedral until late in the 16th century.

COLLECTIONS:

Chiusdino (?), Italy, until 1936; Langton Douglas, London; Dan Fellows Platt, Englewood, New Jersey.

EXHIBITION:

New York, 1955 (E. and A. Silberman).

REFERENCES:

F. M. Perkins, *Rassegna d'Arte,* XI, 1911, p. 5.

G. Di Nicola, *Burlington Magazine,* XXIII, 1913, p. 276.

R. Van Marle, *Italian Schools,* IX, 1927, pp. 334, 357.

L. Venturi, *Pitture Italiane in America,* 1931, pl. CXI.

B. Berenson, *Italian Pictures of the Renaissance,* 1932, p. 512.

G. H. Edgell, *A History of Sienese Painting,* 1932, p. 192.

J. Pope-Hennessy, *Sassetta,* 1939, p. 27.

L. Venturi, 1945, p. 35.

J. Pope-Hennessy, *Sienese Quattrocento Painting,* 1947, p. 25.

F. Zeri, *Burlington Magazine,* XCVIII, 1956, pp. 36–39.

J. Pope-Hennessey, *Burlington Magazine,* XCVIII, 1956, pp. 364–370.

E. Carli, *Sassetta e il Maestro dell'Osservanza,* 1957, pp. 9–13.

23

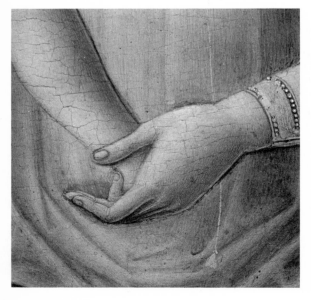

BARTOLOMMEO VIVARINI

(Venetian, 1431/32–c.1491)

The Madonna and Child
Tempera on wood-panel, 45¾ x 25⅞

This superb *Madonna and Child,* perhaps one of Vivarini's earliest independent works, was once the center of a many-panelled altarpiece. In its original form our panel terminated in a pointed Gothic arch, and one must imagine that both above the Virgin's head and below her feet there was originally more space, so that the effect of crowdedness was not as evident as today. The monumentality of the Virgin, serene on her marble throne, is contrasted with the action of the Child, who reaches eagerly for her brooch. The tall pyramidal composition is similar to that of other Vivarini Madonnas such as those of 1471 in the Colonna Collection in Rome, and of 1478 in San Giovanni in Bragora; the compact design of such details as the angel-musicians is characteristic of the painter's best work.

COLLECTIONS:

Nevin, Rome; Ellis, Chicago; Dan Fellows Platt, Englewood, New Jersey.

EXHIBITION:

New York, 1955 (E. and A. Silberman).

REFERENCES:

F. M. Perkins, *Rassegna d'Arte,* VIII, 1908, p. 145.
S. Reinach, *Répertoire,* IV, 1918, pl. 320.
A. Venturi, *Storia dell'Arte Italiana,* VII/3, 1914, p. 326.
B. Berenson, *Venetian Painters,* 1919, p. 14.
L. Venturi, *Pitture Italiane in America,* 1931, pl. CCLVII.
B. Berenson, *Italian Pictures,* 1932, p. 301.
R. Van Marle, *Italian Schools,* XVIII, 1936, p. 106.
B. Fleischmann, in Thieme-Becker, *Allg. Künstler Lexikon,* V, 1940, p. 451.
L. Venturi, 1945, p. 35.
B. Berenson, *Venetian Pictures,* I, 1957, p. 202.

CARLO CRIVELLI

(Venetian, 1430/5–1493/5)

St. Peter

Tempera on wood-panel, 11¼ x 8⅜

The figure fills the frame and seems almost to burst out of it. The head with its gray hair and beard is drawn with strenuous linear vitality. The tendons of his hand stand out as the Saint grasps his key. He holds up a bright scarlet book of Holy Writ, and seems to be exhorting the spectator to hear his message. This half-length figure was perhaps one of a series of panels of saints from the predella of an altar. In style it closely resembles the highly individualized little saints of Crivelli's Monte Fiore Altar, done for the Church of the Frati Conventuali Riformati during the artist's stay in Fermo, about 1470, but the execution is freer.

COLLECTION:

Marinucci, Rome.

REFERENCE:

B. Berenson, *Venetian Pictures,* I, 1957, p. 70.

IACOBVS PAMBARVS BONON PER FRANCIAM AVRIFABRVM HOC OPVS FIERI CVRAVIT 1495

FRANCESCO RAIBOLINI, called FRANCIA

(Bolognese, c. 1450–1517)

The Gambaro Madonna

Oil on wood-panel, 29 x 21½

Inscribed: JACOBVS GAMBARVS BONON[IENSIS] PER FRANCIAM AURIFABRVM HOC OPUS FIERI CVRAVIT 1495 (*Jacopo Gambaro, of Bologna, ordered this work to be made by Francia the goldsmith, 1495*)

As the inscription shows, Francia painted this Madonna in 1495 for Jacopo del Gambaro, his friend and fellow-member of the goldsmith's guild. The goldsmith's approach to art is evident in the precision of the drawing and the jewel-like brilliance of the heavily saturated colors. The feathery trees, sharply delineated Gothic buildings and atmospheric effect of the blue mountains fading into the distance are characteristic of the artist and show the Northern influence which earned him the nickname "Francia". The Madonna has the monumental dignity of Francia's contemporary altarpieces (such as the Bentivoglio Altarpiece of 1499), but there is a notable naturalness in the Child's gesture as He reaches for an apple (symbolizing the Fall) which His Mother holds away from Him.

COLLECTIONS:

Lord Dudley, London; Marquess Pulce Doria, Naples; Quincy Adams Shaw, Boston.

EXHIBITION:

New York, 1955 (E. and A. Silberman).

REFERENCES:

G. F. Waagen, *Kunstwerke und Künstler in England,* II, 1838, p. 204.

Crowe and Cavalcaselle, *History of Painting in North Italy,* II, 1871, p. 274.

B. Berenson, *North Italian Painters,* 1902, p. 223.

A. Venturi, *Storia dell'Arte,* VII, 1914, p. 854; III, p. 881.

L. Venturi, 1945, p. 29.

GIULIANO BUGIARDINI

(Florentine, 1475–1554)

Portrait of Francesco Guicciardini
Oil on wood-panel, 45¼ x 33⅜

It seems likely that Francesco Guicciardini posed for this portrait upon his return to Florence after serving for three years as governor of Bologna. He is shown here seated at his desk, writing his classic history of Italy, completed in 1540 and published posthumously in 1561. Close examination of the sheet before him reveals the opening lines of the work: *"Io ho deliberato di scrive/re le cose accadute alla/ memoria n[ost] ra in Italia. . . ."* ("I have decided to write of things that have happened during our memory in Italy. . . ."). Bugiardini has treated his important subject with care. The meticulous drawing of the face and the volume of the body against the purple drapery make this the artist's masterpiece in portraiture. Details are used to convey an idea of the dignity of the sitter. The fur collar is scrupulously drawn, and the ornate inkwell and elaborately carved chair decorated with the Guicciardini family arms and a fine head *"all' antica"* add to the richness of effect. The painting may be identified with a portrait mentioned by Vasari in his famous *Lives,* and for a time it was in the Medici Palace in Florence.

COLLECTIONS:
Medici, Florence; Prince Alexis Orloff (sold, Galerie Georges Petit, Paris, 1920).
EXHIBITION:
Baltimore Museum of Art, 1939.
REFERENCES:
G. Vasari, *Le Vite dei più eccellenti pittori etc.,* Milanesi ed., VI, p. 205.
L. Venturi, 1945, p. 57.

TIZIANO VECELLIO, called TITIAN

(Venetian, c. 1477/87–1576)

Portrait of a Man
Oil on canvas, 42 x 36¾. Cleaned, 1961
Inscribed: ANNO AETATIS/ SUE XXIV/ TITIAN[O];
(and below) TITIAN[US] F.

As noted in the Introduction, this picture has been recently cleaned. It is now possible to recognize nuances created by the rather limited palette ranging from sharp black and white to warmer brown, rust and flesh tones, the sense of atmospheric depth, and the massive dignity of the aristocratic figure so characteristic of the portraits painted by Titian in the 1540's and '50's. The Rabinowitz painting was apparently once in the Collection of King Charles the First of England. Certainly a picture which could be the duplicate of this one is precisely described in the 17th–century catalogue of that truly outstanding collection published by Vertue in 1757 (see the Introduction). The description indicates that the painting was larger than at present; it undoubtedly included the whole globe which is at the subject's right. This was believed at one time to indicate that the sitter was the geographer Mercator, but of this one cannot be sure today.

Titian's signature appears over the globe. The inscription of Titian's name at the lower left in gold majuscule letters may have been added later.

Before cleaning

COLLECTION:
Believed to have been in the Collection of King Charles I of England.

EXHIBITIONS:
Toledo Museum of Art, 1940; Montreal Art Association, 1942; Williams College, Williamstown, Massachusetts, 1942.

REFERENCES:
G. Vertue, *A Catalogue and Description of King Charles' Capital Collection*, 1757, p. 100.
L. Venturi, 1945, p. 51.
[A. Van der Doort] *Catalogue of the Collection of Charles I,* Walpole Society, XXXVII, 1960, p. 17.

JACOPO ROBUSTI, called IL TINTORETTO

(Venetian, 1518–1594)

Portrait of a Man
Oil on canvas, 48¾ x 37⅛

Against the enveloping shadows and the dark hues of both robe and cap, the features and hands of the seated scholar are boldly highlighted. This emphasis on the face and carefully posed, though unfinished, hands is typical of Tintoretto's portraits; we find it in the Vienna *Portrait of a Man,* dated 1553, and many others such as the *Portrait of Alvise Cornaro* in the Pitti. The highly accented angular folds of the sleeves are also characteristic. However, the treatment of the subject in depth is unusual in Tintoretto's work. The subject usually confronts the viewer directly, close to the picture plane. Here the artist has interposed a table between us and the figure. This sense of distance, as well as the piercing gaze of the subject, give the portrait an intensity of effect which we do not find in the more massive and substantial figures of his earlier paintings. If it is by Tintoretto, the picture must be dated rather late, toward 1570–75. Only the head has been brought to a finished state. The remainder of the canvas is left with the basic ideas of the composition alone brushed in by the artist in a rapid and sketchy fashion.

REFERENCES:
L. Venturi, 1945, p. 53.
H. Tietze, *Tintoretto,* 1948, p. 359.
B. Berenson, *Venetian Pictures of the Renaissance,* 1957, I, p. 176.

HIERONYMUS BOSCH (Netherlandish, c. 1450–1516)

Allegory of Intemperance
Oil on wood-panel, 13 5/16 x 12⅛

The imagery of this striking little panel is graphically concerned with the folly of indulgence in eating and drinking. The tent-like structure to the right bears, as a tavern sign, the cloven hoof of a pig. The lovers within turn their attention not to each other but upon their cup. A mock-Silenus figure—in antique art the portly Silenus was a fixture in the imagery of Bacchic orgies or processions—straddles a cask of wine instead of the traditional ass. Three swimming figures, among them what appears to be a hooded monk, push the floating cask, while a fourth collects the wine spouting from it. Bosch often alluded to proverbs in his paintings; perhaps intended here is a Netherlandish saying which might be translated, "More are drowned in a goblet than in the sea".

Our panel is a fragment from some larger composition. The close similarity of theme, style and scale of figures in this fragment, as well as the dimension of width, with those of the so-called *Ship of Fools* in the Louvre, argue for the theory that the two may once have been actually parts of one ensemble (see below). Perhaps the coat of arms on the tent refers to the original commission. It has been identified as belonging to the De Bergh family of 's Hertogenbosch (where the painter was born and where he worked) and The Hague. A date of 1495–1500 seems likely from the point of view of style.

COLLECTIONS:
Sir Felix Clay Collection, sold London (Christie's, May 11, 1928). In the hands of dealers after 1935 (Malmédé, Cologne; Katz, Dieren, Holland; E. and A. Silberman, New York) before entering the Rabinowitz collection.

EXHIBITIONS:
Rotterdam, 1936, no. 51; Grand Rapids, Michigan, 1940, no. 5; Muskegon, 1941; New York, 1955 (E. and A. Silberman); New Haven, Yale Alumni, 1956; Bruges-Detroit, "Flanders in the Fifteenth Century," 1960.

REFERENCES:
[D. Hannema and J. G. van Gelder] Museum Boymans, Rotterdam, 1936, *Jeroen Bosch, Noord-Nederlandsche Primitieven,* 10 Juli–15 October, 1936, p. 32.
M. J. Friedländer, *Die Altniederländischen Malerei,* XIV, *Peter Bruegel und Nachträge zu den früheren Bänden,* 1937, p. 101.
C. Tolnay, *Hieronymus Bosch,* 1937, p. 90.
L. Baldass, "Zur Entwicklungsgeschichte des Hieronymus Bosch," *Annuaire des Musées Royaux des Beaux Arts de Belgique,* I, 1938, pp. 68–69.
L. Baldass, *Hieronymus Bosch,* 1st ed., 1943, p. 235; and 2nd ed., 1959, pp. 69, 99, note 2; p. 82.
L. Venturi, 1945, pp. 63–64.
J. Combe, *Jérôme Bosch,* 1946, p. 82, no. 40.
J. V. L. Brans, *Hieronymus Bosch (El Bosco en el Prado y en el Escorial),* 1948, p. 44.
D. Bax, *Ontcijfering van Jeroen Bosch,* 1949, p. 199.
[Lotte Brand Philip] Rijksmuseum, Amsterdam, *Middeleeuwse Kunst der Noordelijke Nederlanden,* 28 juni–28 september, 1958 (Amsterdam, 1958), p. 81 (the Louvre "Ship of Fools" and the Rabinowitz panel stated to form perhaps parts of one ensemble).
H. P[auwels] in *Le Siècle des Primitifs Flamands,* Bruges, 26 juin–11 septembre, 1960 (Bruges, 1960), pp. 169–171.
[J. Folie] in *Flanders in the Fifteenth Century,* Detroit, 1960, pp. 206–208 (based on information provided by C. Eisler).

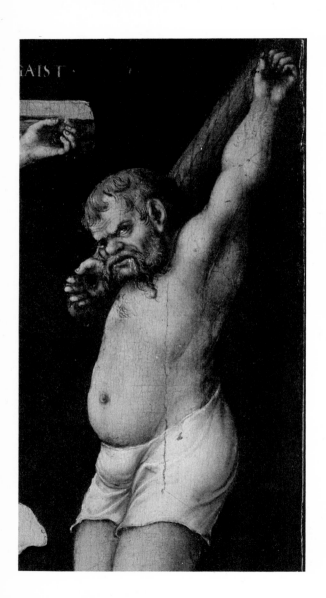

LUCAS CRANACH, THE ELDER

(German, 1472–1533)

Crucifixion with the Converted Centurion
Oil on wood-panel, 23⅜ x 16
Inscribed: Horseman: WARLICH DIESER MENSCH
IS GOTTES SUN GEWEST (Truly this man was the
Son of God—Mark, 16:39); Above the head of
Christ: VATER IN DEIN HENDT BEFIEL ICH MEIN
GAIST (Father into thy hands I commend my
spirit—Luke, 24:46)

Signed with Cranach's winged dragon (bottom right), this panel bears the date 1538. There are two other known versions of the Crucifixion with the converted centurion, one in the Kress Collection in Washington, dated 1536, and the other from 1539 recently in the collection of Prince Lippe in Germany. The popularity of this theme is due to its power to demonstrate a favorite Protestant doctrine that salvation is the gift of God through grace (see the centurion's confession of faith). The figures of the two thieves dramatize the alternative of salvation or damnation. The centurion represents John Frederick (1503–1554), Elector of Saxony, a Protestant prince and Cranach's patron.

COLLECTION:
Count Wilczeck, Vienna.

EXHIBITIONS:
Erfurt, 1905, no. 169; Baltimore Museum of Art, 1939; Grand Rapids Art Gallery, Grand Rapids, Michigan, March, 1941; Montclair Art Museum, Montclair, New Jersey, April, 1941, no. 11; New Haven, Yale Alumni, 1956.

REFERENCES:
M. Doering and H. Voss, *Meisterwerke der Kunst aus Sachsen und Thüringen,* 1905, pl. 27.
M. J. Friedländer and J. Rosenberg, *Gemälde von Lucas Cranach,* 1932, p. 85.
L. Venturi, 1945, pp. 65–66.
[W. E. Suida] *Painting and Sculpture from the Kress Collection,* 1951–1956, Washington National Gallery of Art, 1956, p. 60.

HANS HOLBEIN, THE YOUNGER

(German, 1497/8–1543)

Miniature Portrait of a Young Man
Oil on vellum, 1 1/16 diameter

While working in the Court of Henry VIII of England, Holbein is known to have made a number of portraits in miniature. He most often painted these in watercolor, but the one attributed to him here is in oil. It appears to date from about 1535 and was meant to be worn as a locket, as customary with miniature portraits of the time. The sitter is unknown. Very close in style to this miniature is Holbein's *Self-Portrait* in the Wallace Collection, London. The composition is reproduced at actual size at the right; the enlargement on the left reveals the artist's mastery of the brush, remarkable on so small a scale.

COLLECTION:
Collection L. Michelson, Paris, according to Ganz (see below).
EXHIBITION:
New Haven, Yale Alumni, 1956.
REFERENCES:
L. Venturi, 1945, p. 67.
P. Ganz, *Hans Holbein the Younger,* 1950, p. 258.

SCHOOL OF FONTAINEBLEAU OR OF ANTWERP (16th century)

The Art of Music

Oil on wood-panel, 37¼ x 35⅞

We do not know the artist of this painting, but we do know that it is a close adaptation of the right section of a frescoed lunette in the *Sal de Bal* in the French royal Château of Fontainebleau, decorated between 1550 and 1556 by the Italian painter and sculptor, Primaticcio. The Italian artist placed his plastically modelled figures in a spatially defined composition. The Northern artist who adapted Primaticcio's mural composition in the Rabinowitz panel was possibly French but also possibly an Antwerp Mannerist, such as Maerten de Vos. He played down the plasticity of the figures and spatial setting in order to concentrate on the interweaving of graceful lines and forms on the surface. The subject matter is difficult to interpret. It appears to depict a concert of voices, strings and a triangle. In the background a young, winged nude boy seems to be pushing away an older, heavily draped woman. It is possible that the boy represents the genius of music and that the woman personifies an enemy to the arts, such as Envy or Ignorance. There is another adaptation of the Primaticcio fresco in the Louvre, but the style is quite different—heavier and more classical. The Rabinowitz painting is marked by an engaging spontaneity and varies in degree of finish. In places it shows changes in the drawing underlying lightly applied glazes (see detail at right).

EXHIBITIONS:

Norton Gallery and School of Art, West Palm Beach, 1942; Lawrence Art Museum, Williamstown, Massachusetts, 1942; New Haven, Yale Alumni, 1956.

REFERENCE:

L. Venturi, 1945, pp. 71–72.

ANTON VAN DYCK (Flemish, 1599–1641)

St. Augustine in Ecstasy
Oil on wood-panel, 19⅞ x 12

Shortly after his return from a seven-year stay in Italy Van Dyck completed, in June of 1628, a large Baroque altarpiece for the Church of the Augustinians in Antwerp. This picture, entitled *St. Augustine in Ecstasy,* was soon reproduced in an engraving by the Antwerp artist, Peter de Jode, the Younger. Although executed in a freely brushed and vivid style, the painting in the Rabinowitz collection approaches a highly finished state. Its neutral color-scheme (*grisaille*) turns at times ever so slightly toward rose, gold and lavender-brown in tints of gray. It is thus quite possible that the picture was made as a *"modello"* for the engraver; this was always assumed to be by the master painter himself and only recently has it been questioned (by d'Hulst and Vey, see below). A small oil sketch, apparently for the painting (not the engraving) is preserved in the Ashmolean Museum, Oxford; it differs in respect to several details from the Rabinowitz picture, to which the descriptive word "sketch" can hardly be applied. A pupil's drawing after the Antwerp painting is in the Victoria and Albert Museum, London.

COLLECTIONS:

Methuen, London (catalogued, 1760 and 1805); Baring, London (sale, 1848); Northbrook, London (see below); Christian Holmes, New York.

EXHIBITIONS:

London, Grosvenor Gallery, 1887; Antwerp, 1899; London, Royal Academy, 1900; Amsterdam, 1936.

REFERENCES:

J. Smith, *Catalogue raisonné, etc.,* 1831, III, pp. 3–4.

G. F. Waagen, *Treasures of Art in Great Britain,* 1854, II, p. 182.
J. Guiffrey, *Antoine Van Dyck, Sa Vie et son oeuvre,* 1882, p. 250.
W. H. J. Weale, *Descriptive Catalogue of the Collection of Pictures Belonging to Lord Northbrook,* 1889, p. 88.
L. Cust, *Anthony Van Dyck,* 1900, II, p. 249.
M. Rooses, *Fifty Masterpieces of Anthony Van Dyck,* 1900, p. 42.
E. Schaeffer, *Van Dyck,* 1909, pp. 88, 449.
G. Glück, *Van Dyck,* 1931, p. 544.
L. Venturi, 1945, pp. 77–78.
R.-A. d'Hulst and H. Vey, *Antoon Van Dyck, Tekeningen en olieverfschetsen* (catalogue), Antwerp-Rotterdam, 1960, pp. 157–58 (the Rabinowitz painting attributed to the engraver, Peter de Jode, not to Van Dyck).

47

GIOVANNI BATTISTA TIEPOLO

(Venetian, 1696–1770)

Muse or *Allegory with single figure and vessel*
Oil on canvas, 28 diameter

This roundel in warm, *grisaille* colors against a gilt background, overlaid with abstract floral ornament, belongs with its companion (see next page) to a series of six which were once in the Labia Palace, Venice. The quality of the series as a whole appears to vary from piece to piece. The finest from the point of view of structure of form and drawing, involving as it does so many virtuoso passages of difficult foreshortening, is shown here. It is one of the most beautiful of all Tiepolo's inventive designs, and in few, if any, of his paintings is the total mastery and freedom of the brush more evident.

COLLECTIONS:
Labia Palace, Venice, apparently until 1898; Orefice, Venice; Böhler (1904), Munich.
EXHIBITIONS:
Chicago Art Institute, 1938.
REFERENCES:
P. Molmenti, *Giovanni Battista Tiepolo* (Italian Edition), 1909, p. 73
P. Molmenti (French Edition), 1911, p. 70
D. Rich, *Paintings, Drawings and Prints by the Two Tiepolos,* Chicago Art Institute, 1938, p. 28.

STUDIO (?) OF GIOVANNI BATTISTA TIEPOLO

(Venetian, 1696–1770)

Muse(s) or *Allegory with two figures and mask*
Oil on canvas, 28 diameter

In this pair of figures the drawing is not quite so sure nor the plastic effect so striking as compared to the preceding figure in the series. This roundel may thus be the work of an assistant, perhaps Giovanni Domenico, the great Tiepolo's eldest son. The attribute of a mask held by the figure to the right suggests the Muse of Comic or Tragic Poetry—or perhaps simply an allegory of the theatrical arts. This is clearly not a ceiling decoration, because the background is not the least foreshortened. Like its companions it probably was an over-door or insert in wall-panelling. In such a setting the figures, which imitate sculptures in stucco, were intended to give the illusion of mass when seen from below. Whether the series of roundels was, originally, part of the Labia Palace decoration (see COLLECTIONS, previous entry) is not wholly certain. But there was a tradition still alive at the end of the 19th century asserting their original placement there, and the general style speaks plainly of Tiepolo's manner toward 1750, in other words, just in the period of his recorded activity in the Labia Palace.

COLLECTIONS and REFERENCES as in the previous entry.

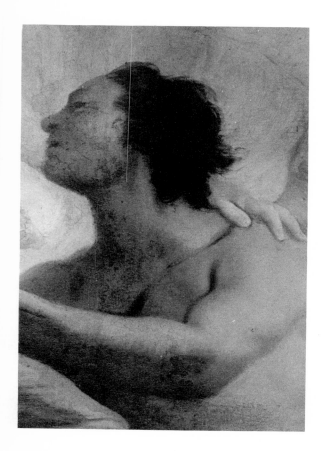

GIOVANNI BATTISTA TIEPOLO
(Venetian, 1696–1770)

and GIOVANNI DOMENICO TIEPOLO
(Venetian, 1727–1804)

Flora and Zephyr
Oil on canvas, 103½ x 81

Between 1750 and 1753 Giovanni Battista Tiepolo with his son, Giovanni Domenico, decorated in fresco both the elaborate Kaisersaal
and great ceremonial stair-hall of the Arch-
bishop's palace in Würzburg, whose architect
was Balthasar Neumann. During this time the
father and son collaborated on other commis-
sions in or near Würzburg. This painting of
Flora and Zephyr belongs to this German period of the two painters and in fact is said to
have come from the private palace of a court
counselor named Hess in Würzburg (the palace now known as the Wittelsbacher Hof).

The subject is an allegory of spring. In
Roman mythology Zephyr personified the mild
west wind and Flora (sometimes his mother,
sometimes his bride) was the deity of flowers
and harbinger of spring, derived from age-old
Italic tradition. The freshness of color and
suavity of rhythms in the design are expres-
sive of Milton's description of the goddess as
an "ever-new delight". The canvas appears to
have been intended for the ceiling of a fair-
sized room, but on an intimate rather than
monumental scale. Giovanni Battista Tiepolo
used the subject both for another ceiling painting (Cà Rezzonico, Venice) and for a design
for sculpture (see the drawing, D 1825.129-
1885, Victoria and Albert Museum, London).

EXHIBITIONS:
Munich, 1913; Berlin, 1918; Berlin, 1927
(Wertheim Gallery) (see below).

REFERENCE:
H. Voss, in *Austellung der Italienischer Malerei
des 17 and 18 Jahrhunderts* (catalogue), Berlin,
1927, p. 26.

PAINTINGS IN THE RABINOWITZ COLLECTION

All dimensions are in inches, height preceding width.

GIOVANNI BELLINI (Venetian, c. 1430–1516)
Madonna and Child
Oil on wood-panel, 13½ x 12⅜ 1959.15.11

BERNARDINO DI BETTO BIAGIO, called IL PINTORICCHIO, attributed to (Umbrian, c. 1435–1513)
Madonna and Child with St. Francis and St. Jerome
Tempera on wood-panel, 16½ x 12⅞
1959.15.16

HIERONYMUS BOSCH (Netherlandish, c.1450–1516)
Allegory of Intemperance (Ills. pp. 37–39)
Oil on wood-panel, 13 5/16 x 12⅛ 1959.15.22

GIULIANO BUGIARDINI (Florentine, 1475–1554)
Portrait of Francesco Guicciardini (Ills. pp. 30–31)
Oil on wood-panel, 45¼ x 33⅜ 1959.15.20

JACOPO DI CIONE (Florentine, mentioned 1365–98)
The Coronation of the Virgin
Tempera on wood-panel, 30⅜ x 21½ 1959.15.2

LUCAS CRANACH, THE ELDER (German, 1472–1533)
Crucifixion with the Converted Centurion (Ills. pp. 40–41)
Oil on wood-panel, 23⅜ x 16 1959.15.23

CARLO CRIVELLI (Venetian, 1430/5–1493/5)
St. Peter (Ills. pp. 26–27)
Tempera on wood-panel, 11¼ x 8⅜
1959.15.15

SIMONE DE' CROCIFISSI (Bolognese, mentioned 1355–1399)
The Crucifixion, and the Coronation of the Virgin
Tempera on wood-panel, 22⅜ x 26¼
1959.15.3

ANTON VAN DYCK (Flemish, 1599–1641)
St. Augustine in Ecstasy (Ills. pp. 46–47)
Oil on wood-panel, 19⅝ x 12 1959.15.26

FLEMISH (?) (16th century)
The Sacrifice of Isaac
Oil on wood-panel, 9¾ x 7½ 1959.15.13b

FLEMISH (?) (16th century)
The Temptation
Oil on wood-panel, 9¾ x 7¼ 1959.15.13a

FLORENTINE (15th century)
The Annunciation (Ills. pp. 18–19)
Tempera on wood-panel, 7½ x 11 1959.15.6

FLORENTINE (third quarter of 15th century)
Man of Sorrows
Tempera on wood-panel, 14⅝ x 13⅝
1959.15.9

FLORENTINE (15th century)
Marriage Salver (Ills. pp. 20–21)
Tempera on wood-panel, 22⅞ diameter
1959.15.8

SCHOOL OF FONTAINEBLEAU OR OF ANTWERP (16th century)
The Art of Music (Ills. pp. 44–45)
Oil on wood-panel, 37¼ x 35⅞ 1959.15.25

FRANCESCO DEI FRANCESCHI (Venetian, active c. 1450)
Flight of the Soldiers Sent to Capture St. Mammas
Tempera on wood-panel, 18¾ x 14 1946.72

FRANCESCO DEI FRANCESCHI (Venetian, active
  c. 1450)
St. Mammas Thrown to the Beasts
Tempera on wood-panel, 18¾ x 14   1946.73

GIOVANNI DI MARCO, called DAL PONTE
  (Florentine, 1385–1437)
St. James Major and Resurrection (Ills. pp.
16–17)
St. John the Baptist and Crucifixion (Ills. pp.
16–17)
Tempera on wood-panels, 50¼ x 13 (St. James
Major and Resurrection); 50⅛ x 12⅞ (St.
John the Baptist and Crucifixion).
                                1959.15.7a–b

HANS HOLBEIN, THE YOUNGER (German,
  1497/8–1543)
Miniature Portrait of a Young Man (Ills. pp.
42–43)
Oil on vellum, 1 1/16 diameter   1959.15.24

PIETRO LORENZETTI (Sienese, active 1320–1348)
*St. Andrew and St. James the Greater with a
Prophet* (Ills. pp. 12–13)
Tempera on wood-panel, 14½ x 8½ (St. An-
drew); 14⅝ x 8⅝ (St. James the Greater);
22 x 21½ (frame, with Prophet)   1959.15.7a–b

NICCOLO DI SEGNA (?) (Sienese, active about
  1330–1340)
Madonna and Child (Ills. pp. 10–11)
Tempera on wood-panel, 45½ x 28¼
                                1959.15.17

FRANCESCO RAIBOLINI, called FRANCIA
  (Bolognese, c. 1450–1517)
The Gambaro Madonna (Ills. pp. 28–29)
Oil on wood-panel, 29 x 21½   1959.15.10

SCHOOL OF RIMINI (mid-14th century). For-
merly attributed to Giovanni Baronzio
The Coronation of the Virgin
Tempera on wood-panel, 36⅝ x 23½
                                1959.15.14

JACOPO ROBUSTI, called IL TINTORETTO
  (Venetian, 1518–1594)
Portrait of a Man (Ills. pp. 34–35)
Oil on canvas, 48¾ x 37⅛   1959.15.19

STEFANO DI GIOVANNI, called SASSETTA
  (Sienese, mentioned 1423–1450)
The Virgin Annunciate (Ills. pp. 22–23)
Tempera on wood-panel, 23¼ x 19⅜ 1959.15.5

GIOVANNI BATTISTA TIEPOLO (Venetian,
  1696–1770)
Muse or *Allegory with single figure and vessel*
(Ills. pp. 48–49)
Oil on canvas, 28 diameter   1947.17

GIOVANNI BATTISTA TIEPOLO (Venetian,
  1696–1770) and GIOVANNI DOMENICO TIEPOLO
  (Venetian, 1727–1804)
Flora and Zephyr (Ills. pp. 52–53)
Oil on canvas, 103½ x 81   1959.15.21

STUDIO (?) OF GIOVANNI BATTISTA TIEPOLO
  (Venetian, 1696–1770)
Muse(s) or *Allegory with two figures and
mask* (Ills. pp. 50–51)
Oil on canvas, 28 diameter   1947.18

TIZIANO VECELLIO, called TITIAN (Venetian,
  c. 1477/87–1576)
Portrait of a Man (Ills. pp. 32–33)
Oil on canvas, 42 x 36¾   1959.15.18

PAOLO VENEZIANO (Venetian, active about
  1320–1360)
St. Mary Magdalen and *St. John the Baptist*
(Ills. pp. 14–15)
Tempera on wood-panels, 23 x 9⅜ (St. Mary
Magdalen); 23¼ x 9¼ (St. John the Baptist)
                                1959.15.4a–b

BARTOLOMMEO VIVARINI (Venetian,
  1431/32–c. 1491)
The Madonna and Child (Ills. pp. 24–25)
Tempera on wood-panel, 45¾ x 25⅞
                                1959.15.12

Two thousand copies of this monograph have been printed by the Meriden Gravure Company in April 1961 through the generosity of Hannah D. Rabinowitz. Design by Norman Ives. Photography by Emiddio De Cusati. Composition by Connecticut Printers, Inc.